Little Bear's
Colors & Shapes

Little Bear's
Colors & Shapes

JANE HISSEY

BARNES
&NOBLE
BOOKS

Little Bear's
Colors

red orange yellow green blue

red balloon

Bramwell has given Jolly a long **red** scarf.

orange yellow green blue purple

orange pumpkin

pink brown black white red

Jolly is painting with **orange** paint.

yellow **wool**

brown **black** white **red** orange

Hoot is sharing her yellow cheese.

green blue purple pink brown

green umbrella

black white red orange yellow

What is the green monkey eating?

blue purple pink brown black

blue bone

Little Bear is standing on a **blue** chair.

purple hat

red orange yellow green blue

Jolly has caught two **purple** balloons.

pink brown black white red

pink blanket

orange yellow green blue purple

Lizzie Long Ears is wearing a **pink** dress.

brown black white red orange

brown monkey

The bears are cozy in their **brown** basket.

black white red orange yellow

black cat

The **black** dog is hiding his rubber bones.

white red orange yellow green

white box

blue purple pink brown black

Old Bear is cutting out white decorations.

stripes

black and white **stripes**

Can you find the **stripy** socks?

spots

black **spots**

How many **spotty** things can you see?

checks

checkered bow

Little Bear's boat has a **checkered** sail.

Which **colors** and **patterns** can you find?

Little Bear's
Shapes

square   circle   triangle   rectangle   star   semi-circle

square

square flag

cube   sphere   pyramid   cone   cuboid   cylinder

The toys are cutting out square windows.

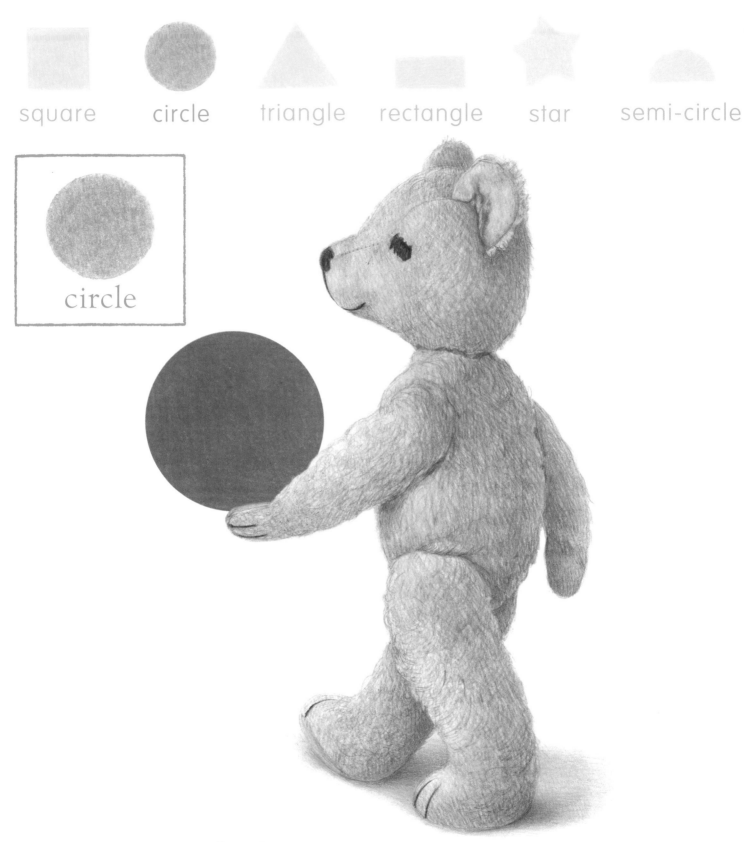

square   circle   triangle   rectangle   star   semi-circle

circle

blue circle

cube   sphere   pyramid   cone   cuboid   cylinder

Bruno's hula hoop is a circle.

square   circle   **triangle**   rectangle   star   semi-circle

triangle

red triangle

Little Bear's dragon mask has triangles for teeth.

square circle triangle **rectangle** star semi-circle

rectangle

See-through rectangle

cube   sphere   pyramid   cone   cuboid   cylinder

The bears are all holding paper rectangles.

square   circle   triangle   rectangle   star   semi-circle

star

paper star

cube   sphere   pyramid   cone   cuboid   cylinder

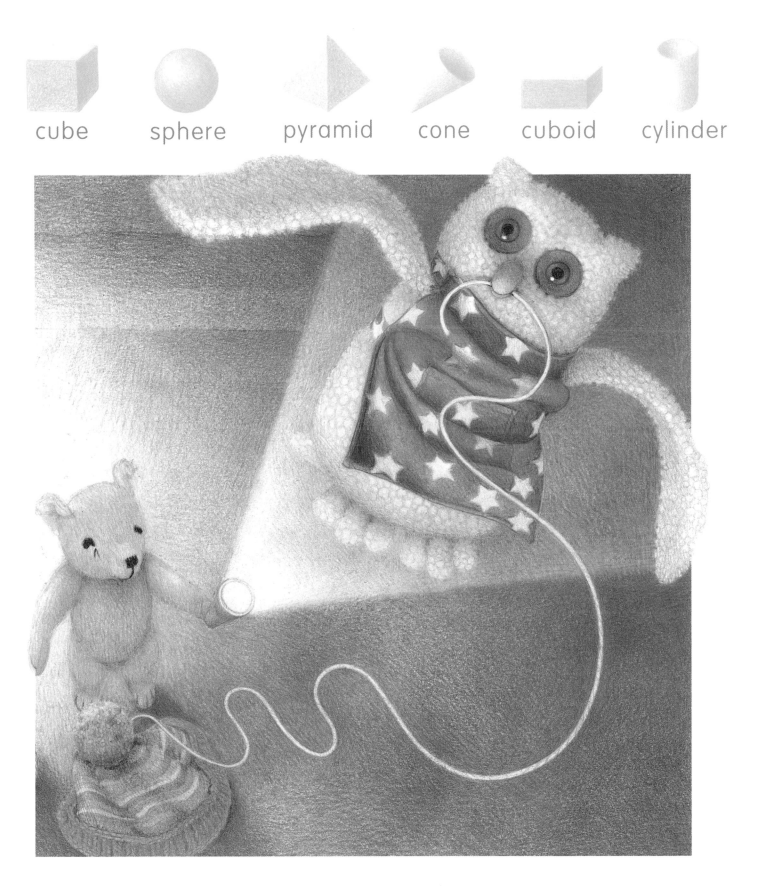

Hoot has stars on her apron.

square circle triangle rectangle star semi-circle

semi-circle

biscuit semi-circles

cube sphere pyramid cone cuboid cylinder

Teddy is pointing to a yellow semi-circle.

These are all two-dimensional —
2-D — shapes. They are flat.

These are all three-dimensional –
3-D – shapes. They are not flat.

square   circle   triangle   rectangle   star   semi-circle

cube

wooden cubes

cube   sphere   pyramid   cone   cuboid   cylinder

Ruff's birthday cake is a cube.

square · circle · triangle · rectangle · star · semi-circle

sphere

glass sphere

cube sphere pyramid cone cuboid cylinder

The ball the toys have found is a sphere.

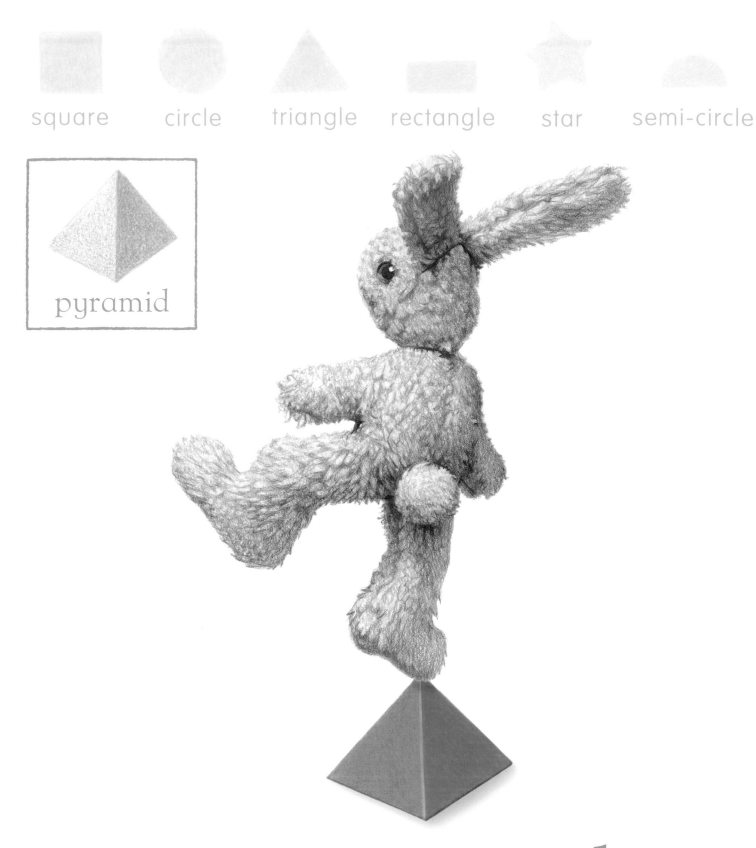

square   circle   triangle   rectangle   star   semi-circle

pyramid

green pyramid

cube   sphere   **pyramid**   cone   cuboid   cylinder

Camel is galloping past some pyramids.

square   circle   triangle   rectangle   star   semi-circle

cone

ice-cream cones

cube sphere pyramid **cone** cuboid cylinder

Little Bear and Ruff have cone-shaped hats.

square　　circle　　triangle　　rectangle　　star　　semi-circle

cuboid

cuboid suitcase

cube sphere pyramid cone **cuboid** cylinder

Sarah Elizabeth's sewing box is a cuboid.

square   circle   triangle   rectangle   star   semi-circle

cylinder

wooden cylinder

cube　　sphere　　pyramid　　cone　　cuboid　　cylinder

Teddy's rolling pin is a cylinder.

How many shapes
can you find?

For Richard, Karen, Rowena
and Susan and John

2003 Barnes & Noble Books

ISBN 0-7607-4266-9

10 9 8 7 6 5 4 3 2 1

RANDOM HOUSE CHILDREN'S BOOKS
61–63 Uxbridge Road, London W5 5SA
A division of The Random House Group Ltd

RANDOM HOUSE AUSTRALIA (PTY) LTD
20 Alfred Street, Milsons Point, Sydney,
New South Wales 2061, Australia

RANDOM HOUSE NEW ZEALAND LTD
18 Poland Road, Glenfield, Auckland 10, New Zealand

RANDOM HOUSE (PTY) LTD
Endulini, 5A Jubilee Road, Parktown 2193, South Africa

THE RANDOM HOUSE GROUP Limited Reg. No. 954009

A CIP catalogue record for this book is available from the British Library.

Printed in Singapore